Compiled and edited by Andy Jones and Arthur Dick

The Complete Blues Guitar Player: Book 2

Exclusive Distributors:
Music Sales Limited, 8/9 Frith Street, London W1V 5TZ, England.
Music Sales Pty Limited, 120 Rothschild Avenue, Rosebery, NSW 2018, Australia.

Order No. AM91084
ISBN 0-7119-3415-0
This book © Copyright 1993 by Wise Publications

Book design by Studio Twenty, London
Computer management by Adam Hay Editorial Design
Cover photography by Julian Hawkins

Music processed by The Pitts

Printed in the United Kingdom by
J.B. Offset Printers (Marks Tey) Limited, Marks Tey, Essex.

Your Guarantee of Quality
As publishers, we strive to produce every book to the highest commercial standards. The music has been freshly
engraved and the book has been carefully designed to minimise awkward page turns and to make playing from it a real pleasure.
Particular care has been given to specifying acid-free, neutral-sized paper made from pulps which have not been elemental chlorine
bleached. This pulp is from farmed sustainable forests and was produced with special regard for the environment.
Throughout, the printing and binding have been planned to ensure a sturdy, attractive publication which should give years of enjoyment. If
your copy fails to meet our high standards, please inform us and we will gladly replace it.

Music Sales' complete catalogue lists thousands of titles and is free from your local music shop,
or direct from Music Sales Limited. Please send a cheque/postal order for £1.50 for postage to:
Music Sales Limited, Newmarket Road, Bury St. Edmunds, Suffolk IP33 3YB.

Wise Publications
London/New York/Paris/Sydney/Copenhagen/Madrid

Tablature & Instructions Explained

The tablature stave comprises six lines, each representing a string on the guitar as illustrated.

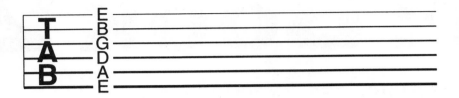

A number on any of the lines indicates, therefore, the string and fret on which a note should be played.

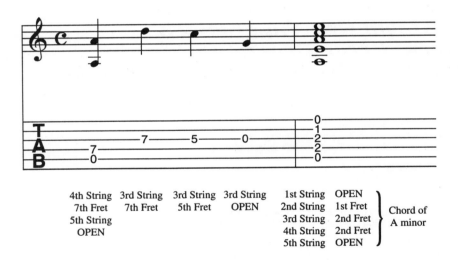

4th String	3rd String	3rd String	3rd String	1st String	OPEN	
7th Fret	7th Fret	5th Fret	OPEN	2nd String	1st Fret	Chord of
5th String				3rd String	2nd Fret	A minor
OPEN				4th String	2nd Fret	
				5th String	OPEN	

A useful hint to help you read tablature is to cut out small squares of self-adhesive paper and stick them on the upper edge of the guitar neck adjacent to each of the frets, numbering them accordingly. Be careful to use paper that will not damage the finish on your guitar.

Finger Vibrato

Tremolo Arm Vibrato

Glissando

Strike the note, then slide the finger up or down the fretboard as indicated.

Tremolo Strumming

This sign indicates fast up and down stroke strumming.

8va

This sign indicates that the notes are to be played an octave higher than written.

loco

This instruction cancels the above.

This note-head indicates the string is to be totally muted to produce a percussive effect.

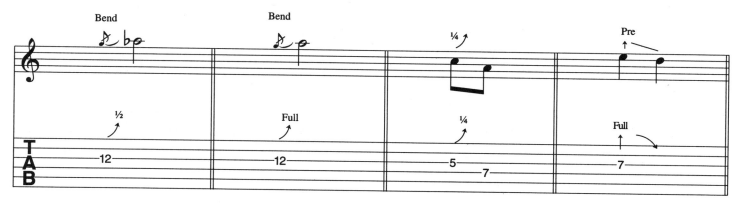

HALF TONE BEND

Play the note G then bend the string so that the pitch rises by a half tone (semi-tone).

FULL TONE BEND

DECORATIVE BEND

PRE-BEND

Bend the string as indicated, strike the string and release.

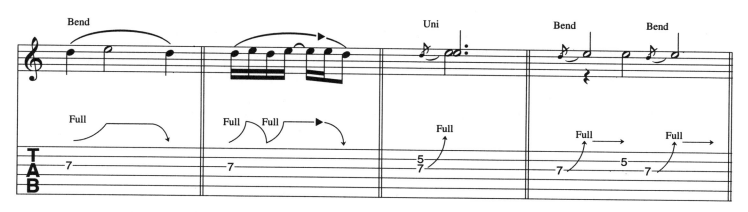

BEND & RELEASE

Strike the string, bend it as indicated, then release the bend whilst it is still sounding.

BEND & RESTRIKE

Strike the string, bend or gliss as indicated, then restrike the string where the symbol occurs.

UNISON BEND

Strike both strings simultaneously then immediately bend the lower string as indicated.

STAGGERED UNISON BEND

Strike the lower string and bend as indicated; whilst it is still sounding strike the higher string.

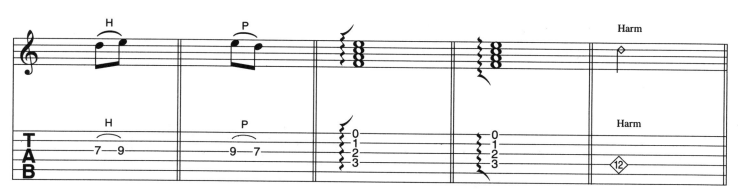

HAMMER-ON

Hammer a finger down on the next note without striking the string again.

PULL-OFF

Pull your finger off the string with a plucking motion to sound the next note without striking the string again.

RAKE-UP

Strum the notes upwards in the manner of an arpeggio.

RAKE-DOWN

Strum the notes downwards in the manner of an arpeggio.

HARMONICS

Strike the string whilst touching it lightly at the fret position shown. Artificial Harmonics, (A.H.), will be described in context.

The Blues

What makes a great blues solo? Is it the melody line, the phrasing, or the bending and vibrato attached to the notes? A knowledge of your scales is an obvious advantage, so too is the ability to turn the scales into useful phrases. Beyond this your technique has to be able to deliver the goods, but how you do this is up to you. Each player has his or her own statement to make and an individual voice with which to make it.

The beginning of this book deals with the most commonly used scales. It is important that you become familiar with using scales, as the following music examples show how they are used by famous blues players. If you are unsure which scale is which, always refer back to this section.

The analysis of these great players' ideas provides a valuable insight and inspiration for you to learn from. Blues playing, however, is heartfelt and emotive music. It goes beyond the actual notes played, and relies heavily on the more expressive techniques such as bends and vibratos to get the true 'feel'.

There is no substitute for listening to the real greats, learning from their skills and then applying them to your own playing. The musical extracts in this book are taken from available recordings, so read the music and, above all - listen!

To begin with let's look at some of the theory behind the blues. We will look at two vital areas

- The chord progressions and chord types that are used

- The scales which match these chords and progressions

This is all the basic information you will need to be able to play the blues. Armed with this we will be able to explore some of the classic blues riffs and phrases.

Classic Blues Progressions - The Twelve Bar And Eight Bar Blues

The blues sequence commonly falls into a twelve bar pattern, though a smaller eight bar version is also widely used.

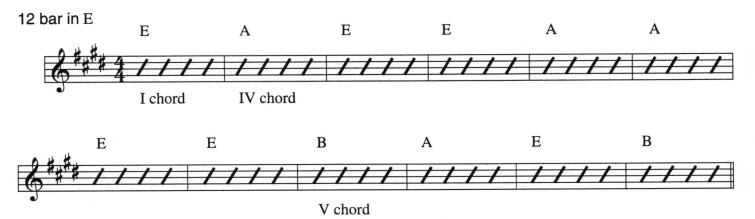

8 bar in E

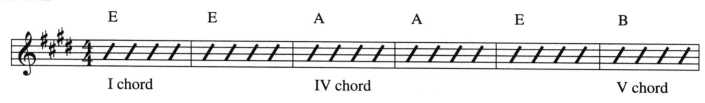

I chord   IV chord   V chord

There are seven different notes in the major scale (in the scale of E these notes are E, F#, G#, A, B, C#, and D#). These degrees of the scale can be numbered I – VII, and their respective chords given these numbers. For example, in the key of E, chord IV is the chord of A. You don't need a degree in nuclear physics to work out that, by using numbers instead of names, we can easily transpose this system into other keys.

In the key of C (whose scale is made up of all the white notes on the piano C, D, E, F, G, A, and B) the fourth degree of the scale is the note F, so chord IV in the key of C is the chord of F. A word of warning: the chords in a major scale are made up of different chord types – a blend of major (strong) chords, minor chords (weak) and a diminished chord on the seventh degree. You don't need to know why this is, as long as you are aware of the different types.

The chords built on all major scales conform to this pattern

Scale	I	II	III	IV	V	VI	VII*
Chord type	Major	Minor	Minor	Major	Major	Minor	Diminished

* In the blues the seventh degree of the scale (and therefore its chord) is flattened to take away the sharp edges of the music. The flattened 7th is the most common 'blue' note and, as such is generally taken as read when talking about sevenths.

In the above examples the relationship between chords I, IV and V is the same, consequently most riffs and phrases will work in both. Let's stick to using the twelve bar sequence as a vehicle for our ideas; we'll assume that these ideas will work equally well over the shorter eight bar pattern.

As we've already found out, one of the primary characteristics of the blues sound is the flattened 7th. We can add flattened 7ths to all the chords in the progression to give them a 'bluesy' feel. These are so common that they are referred to as just '7ths', not minor or flattened 7ths.

There are many variants on the blues, though the most common version is as follows:

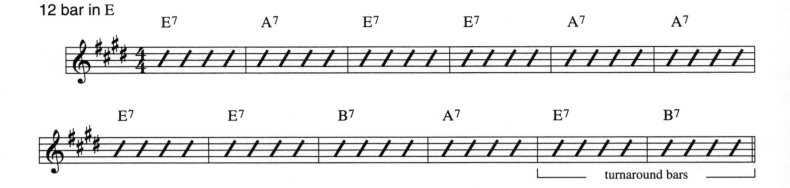

12 bar in E

The two turnaround bars act as a means of taking the piece back to its beginning and, as you will see, there are various permutations of chords available in these two bars (especially in jazz chord progressions or 'changes'). Similarly, we can use the turnaround bars as an introduction to a twelve bar.

Before moving on to single line scales and phrases it is important that you understand the rhythm of the blues style. The 'Blues Shuffle' is so called because of the feel of the groove. On many charts this is notated by ♪♩ = ♩♪ above the first bar, which is an indication that the rhythms should be played with a swinging, or shuffle style.

A typical twelve bar rhythm accompaniment might be played using the 4th, 5th and 6th strings. Use the palm of your right hand (pick hand) to damp the strings, creating a more precise and controlled rhythm.

We have already seen that the simplest turnaround consists of chord V going to chord I, and these can be decorated in a blues style by adding 7ths to the chords. We can further decorate the turnaround by inserting chord IV, thus, in E, the progression changes to:

$$E^7 \; / \; A^7 \; / \; E^7 \; / \; B^7 \; / \; :\|$$

or add chromatic movement to get to the V7 chord:

$$E^7 \; / \; A^7 \; / \; E^7 \quad A^7 \quad A^{\#7} \quad B^7 \; :\|$$

More 'Blue Notes'

The key of E has four sharps in its key signature*. However, the characteristic 7th flavour of the blues dictates that we should modify the scale accordingly.

D♮ is the 7th

This is where we start to explore the world of modes. Make sure you know all your major and minor scales before getting into this – it will make your life much easier in the long run!

This is in fact the Mixolydian mode, and is equivalent to playing A major, starting on the Vth degree of the scale.

Although this mode provides the flattened 7th there is another important blue note which we will need, and this is the flattened 3rd.

G♮ is the ♭3rd

This is equivalent to beginning on the second degree of the D major scale. It is in fact the E Dorian mode. Against an E7 chord in our sequence this mode works very well.

Although major and minor scale types will work, they do not lend themselves to the Chicago, Delta or Texas blues styles, as the scales used in these styles are derived from jazz. So, instead of the major, minor and modal systems we use other scales. For the blues in E they are

Fig. 1. E major pentatonic

Fig. 2. E minor pentatonic

Fig. 3. E minor blues

* Sometimes the key signature is omitted when discussing a blues to avoid the continuous use of accidentals.

The Major Pentatonics

The primary chords available from the harmonised major scale are the chords I, IV and V, so we can employ the A and B major pentatonics as well. The D major scale (E Dorian, remember) generates another useful pentatonic. Check out the following:

Play the above pentatonic lines against an E7 chord – you will notice that they each create different and interesting colours against the same chord. All these examples are good, though the E major pentatonic scale is the 'bluesiest', and therefore most commonly used.

The Minor Pentatonics

Like the preceding major scales, E minor pentatonic is also a five note scale, though this time the flattened 3rd and 7th are both present. This provides an even more 'bluesy' feel. As you will probably notice, many blues phrases use minor pentatonics, or a combination of major and minor pentatonics.

Minor chords II, III and VI (F#m, G#m and C#m in the key of E) can also provide pentatonic alternatives.

I major pentatonic	has the same notes as	**VI minor pentatonic**.
Emaj (E, F#, G#, B, C#)		C#min (C#, E, F#, G#, B)
IV major pentatonic	has the same notes as	**II minor pentatonic**
Amaj (A, B, C#, E, F#)		F#min (F#, A, B, C#, E)
V major pentatonic	has the same notes as	**III minor pentatonic**
Bmaj (B, C#, D#, F#, G#)		G#min (G#, B, C#, D#, F#)

You will notice that we are really seeing the use of related chords within the E major 'orbit'. The most commonly used major pentatonic for the blues in E is the E major pentatonic; this also applies to its relative minor (C# minor).

We have already seen that the E minor pentatonic, by virtue of its flattened 3rd and flattened 7th, creates the most 'bluesy' sound.

We can now add the final colour to our musical palette by including perhaps the 'bluesiest' note of all – the flattened 5th. By adding this note to the minor pentatonic we get a six note scale, which will open the door to a wealth of blues licks.

Em pentatonic   Em blues

This scale is called the **Minor Blues Scale**.

As you will have gathered by now, similar blues scales can be created from our other minor pentatonics (F#m, G#m and C#m).

Even though the flattened 5th is not normally associated with the major scale, it is such a strong and emotive sound that your ear will readily accept it. In exactly the same way as the addition of the flattened 5th to the minor pentatonic forms the minor blues scale, so the same process with the major pentatonic gives us the **Major Blues Scale.**

E pentatonic   E blues

For the time being let's simplify matters by concentrating on the minor pentatonic and the minor blues scales. This doesn't mean we will disregard the major scales – you should always be aware of the relationship between the major and minor forms of the scale.

From what we have learned so far we can see that, for a blues in E, the following scales are most commonly used:

- Em pentatonic

- Em blues

- C♯m pentatonic (same as E pentatonic)

- C♯m blues (same as E Blues)

Let's now take a look at the positions on the fretboard where these scales are played. You will see that each scale forms a pattern over the fretboard; you will quickly learn these finger patterns, making it easier to use these scales when constructing blues phrases, and when transposing into new keys. By adapting these finger patterns you can work other scales into your licks.

Here are the basic scales for the blues in E:

Em pentatonic

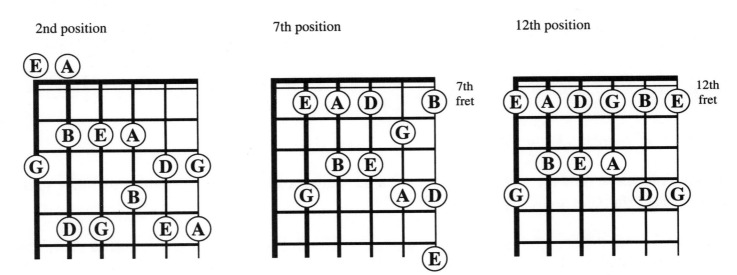

Em blues

Open position

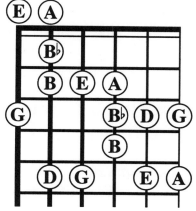

7th position

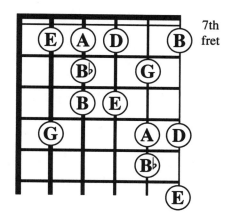

12th position

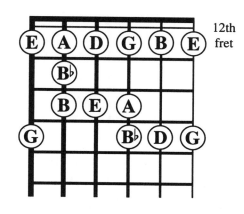

C#m pentatonic

4th position

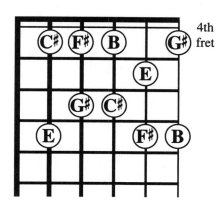

9th position

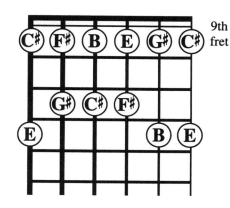

11th position

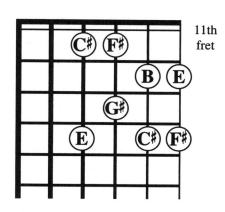

C#m blues

4th position

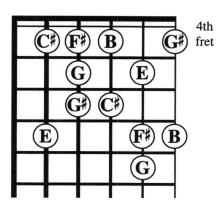

9th position

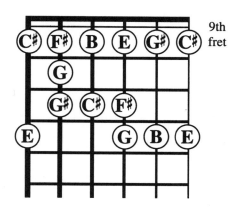

11th position

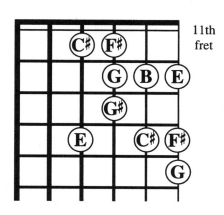

Many blues phrases will involve not just one scale, but fragments from several. Take one position on the fretboard and get used to playing the scales one after another, mixing them up. You will need to become as familiar as possible with them so that, when you learn a new phrase, you will understand where it comes from. More crucially, you will be able to take riffs and phrases and work them in to other scales and other keys. These scale shapes will form the foundation of your ability to express yourself in the blues. Spend some time on this stuff – it's important! Learn these scales well or you will pay the price later in frustration for yourself and predictably boring playing for the musicians you play with.

Now go back to the blues on page 6. The scales we have been looking at relate to chord I (or I7), but what about chords IV and V?

The Em pentatonic and blues scales can be played over all the changes in the progression. The major (and relative minor) pentatonic and blues scales can also be used for chords IV (A/F#m scales) and V (B/G#m scales).

Further options are available, for example the Mixolydian and Dorian modes work well. Use A Mixolydian and A Dorian over the A7 chord and B Mixolydian and B Dorian over the B7 chord.

As you look at the following solos you must always bear in mind the blues style. This is achieved with a combination of special techniques such as vibratos and bends. As you listen to more blues guitar you will pick up a sense of style which is common to all players, and then some quirks of style which are peculiar to certain individual artists. It's up to you to take what you want from what's out there.

Remember to experiment with all the phrases you learn – the key to good musicianship is flexibility, so try out as many variations as you can. Try transposing the riffs into different keys, or playing them at different octaves. You may experiment with tempo, feel, or groove, to evoke different moods and colours with the music.

Above all – have fun!

Pretty Woman
Albert King

CD 'King Of The Blues Guitar'
Atlantic 8213 – 2

Words & Music by A.C. Williams

Albert King's cool and relaxed solo seems to show that he's not out to impress. We could learn a lot about timing and phrasing from Albert King. Although his vibrato is wide, he never seems to overdo it.

His bending is worth hearing. At bar 7, he makes a very precise bend from B♭ to D♭ on the 2nd string. At bar 11 his bends hover between C and D♭s, from a fretted B♭.

The last two bars of the solo are a stock blues ending and can be used in many other songs.

Solo

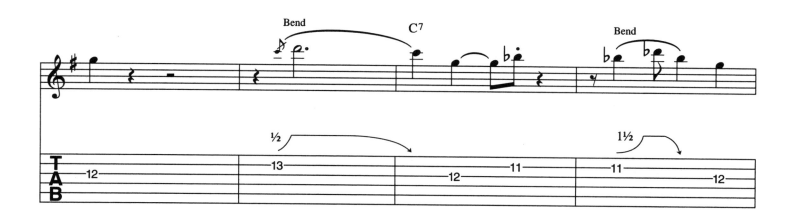

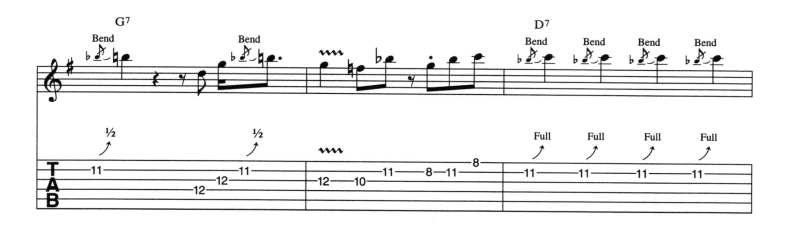

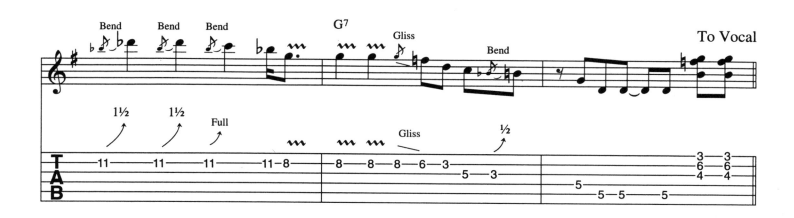

Example 1 shows the bass riff. This pattern is moved to follow the chord changes. Note that like 'Born Under A Bad Sign' this riff uses the flattened 3rd.

Example 1

Example 2 shows the figure played by the horns behind Albert's solo. Here we approach the major 3rd and flattened 7th degrees from a semitone, 1 fret, below. This is a common device and translates well to the guitar – you can use this idea over any regular blues progression.

Example 3 shows the same backing figure as played over the C7 chord.

Example 2

Example 3

Five Long Years
Buddy Guy

LP 'Damn Right, I've Got The Blues'
ORE LP516

Words & Music by Eddie Boyd

Buddy makes frequent use of the blues scale — so much so that the major 3rd is rarely used, even over the tonic chord.

In Example 1, Buddy plays an ear-catching phrase which slides way up the 3rd string. Try practising playing along one string — it will help you break the habit of staying in one position or range. This unusual phrase seems to indicate that Buddy is really improvising here — thinking on his feet.

Example 1

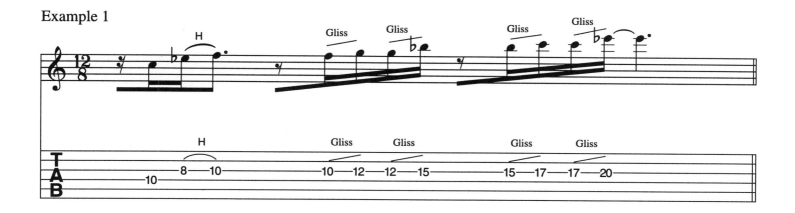

Example 2 is designed to help your bending become more accurate. Practise bending F on the 3rd string up to G making sure that you bend all the way. Keep checking the tuning on your bent notes with their fretted equivalents.

Example 2

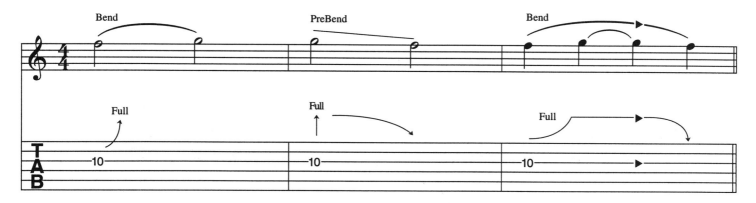

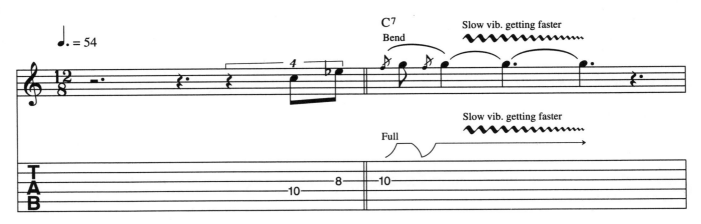

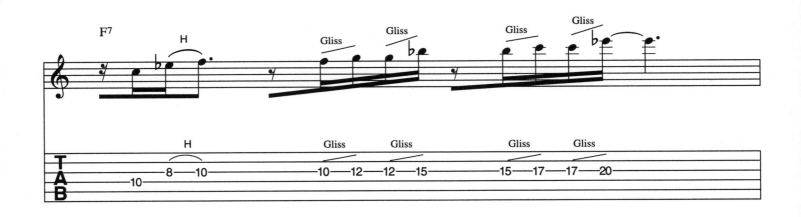

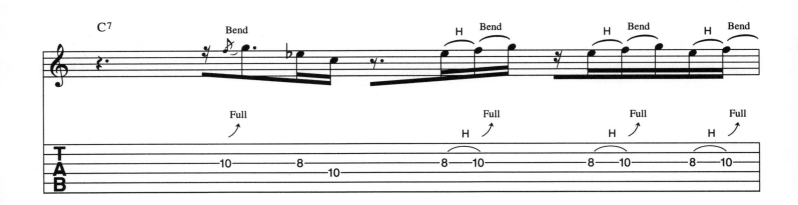

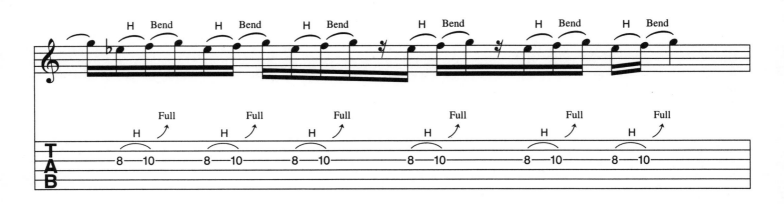

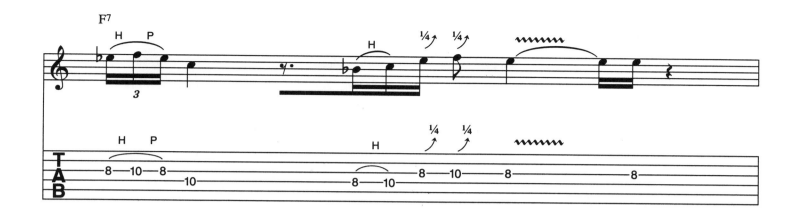

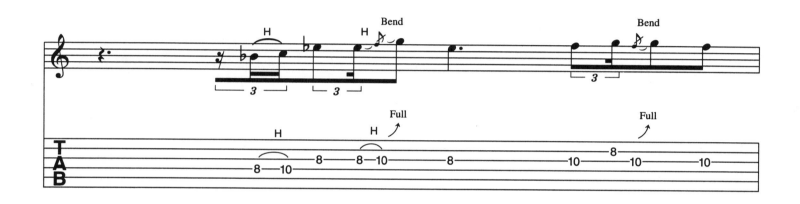

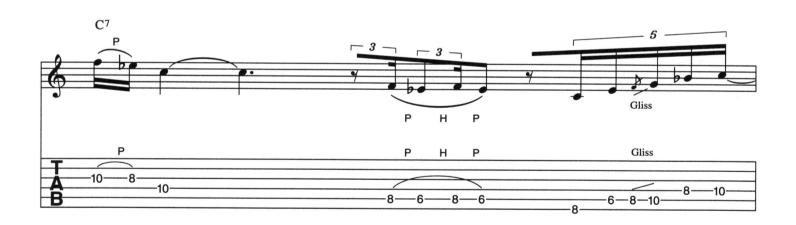

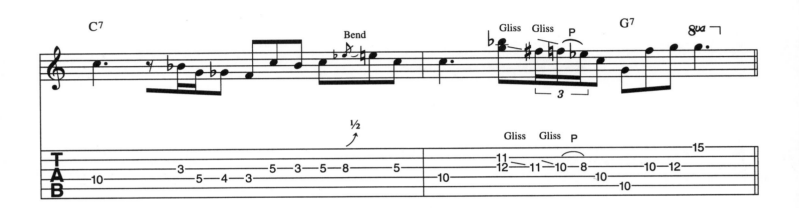

Stop Messin' Around
Gary Moore

CD 'Still Got The Blues'
Virgin CDV 2612

Words & Music by Green & Adams

I have notated Gary Moore's solo on 'Stop Messin' Around' in $\frac{4}{4}$ for ease of reading, but if you listen to the recording the feel has a swing pulse. The quavers are played with a swing feel directed by the ♩♪ symbol at the beginning of the music.

Although Gary has obviously listened to the great blues players, his sense of pulse is firmly hooked onto the beat.

Bar 3 shows one of the most common blues/rock devices — you'll know it when you hear it!

Solo

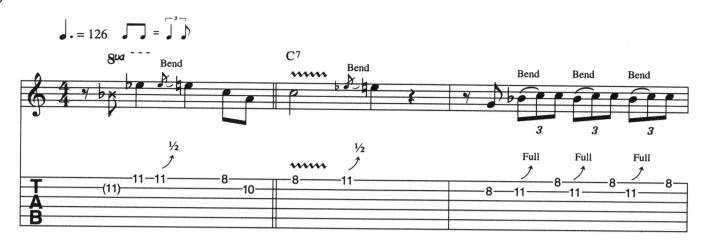

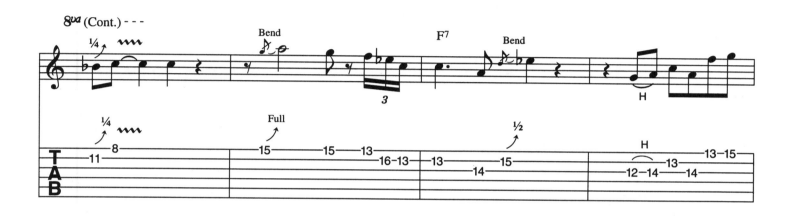

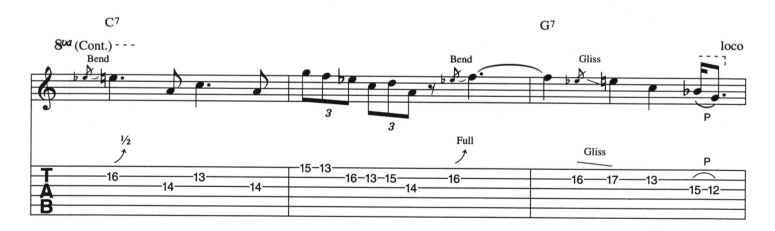

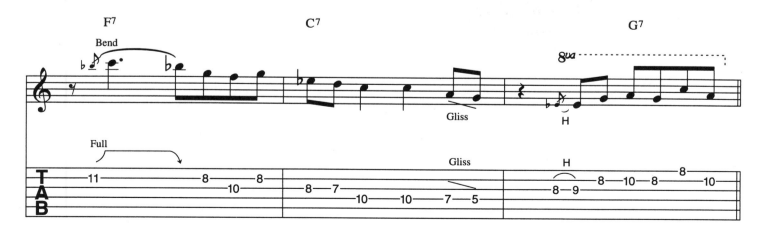

The Welfare (Turns Its Back On You)
Robert Cray

CD 'The Score'
Charly Blues Masterworks Vol.16 BM16

Words & Music by Sonny Thompson & Lucious Weaver

This Robert Cray solo typifies his style – it is soulful, yet intricate, and its rhythmic variety gives it the quality of an impassioned speech.

Cray's sense of rhythmic pulse is freer than that of most of his contemporaries. He seems to glide effortlessly over the more rhythmic groove of the rhythm section.

In this area, his debt to blues masters such as Buddy Guy is clear.

It is worth noting the clarity of his sound — he doesn't feel the need to crank up the distortion to create an effect.

Solo

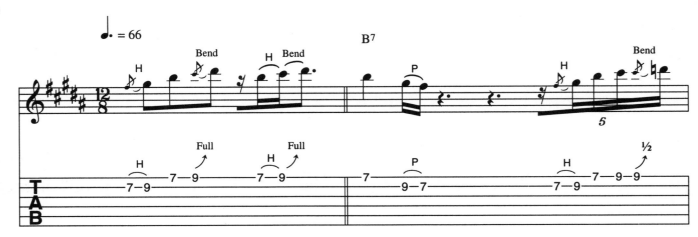

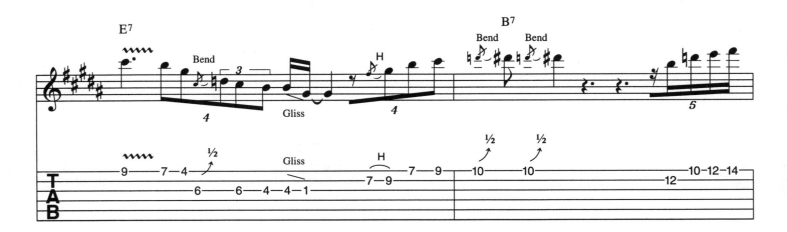

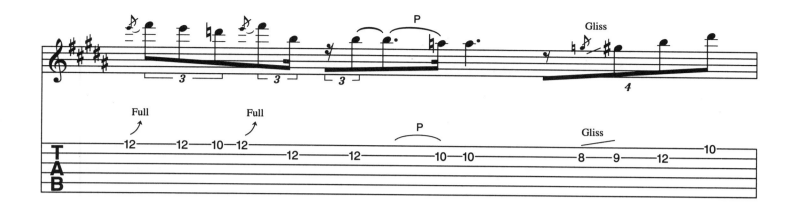

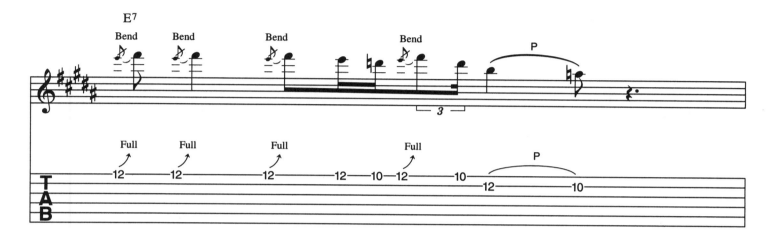

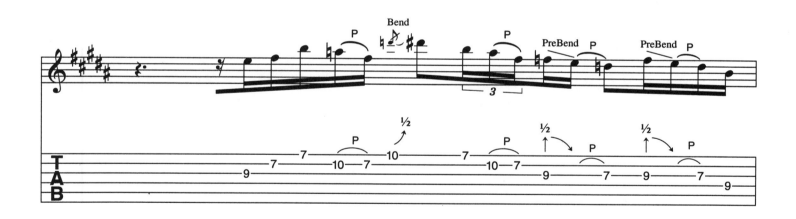

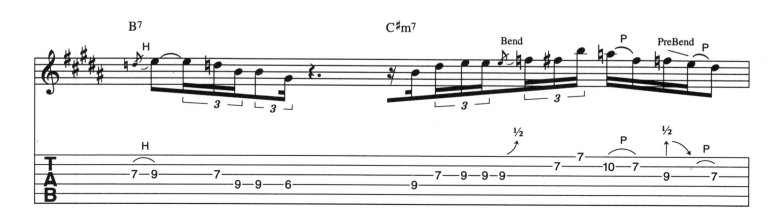

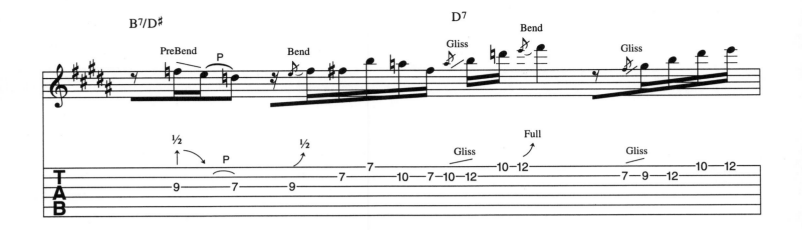

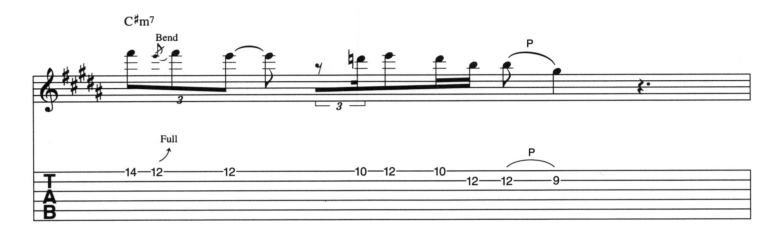

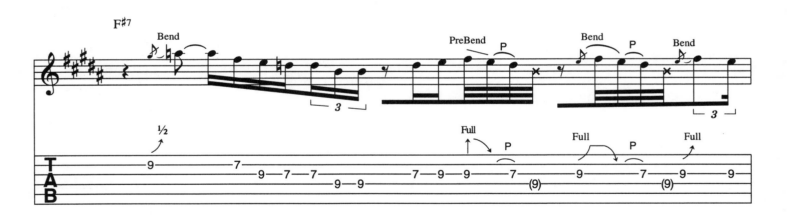

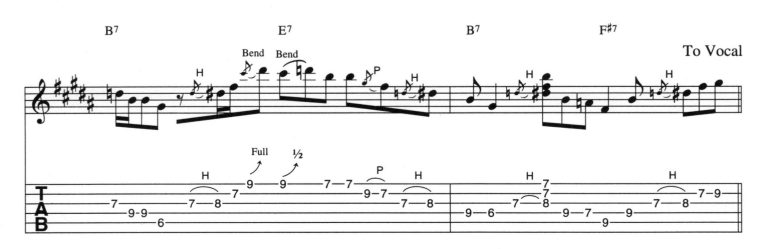

22

Texas Flood
Stevie Ray Vaughan

LP 'Texas Flood'
Sony 460951

Words & Music by Joseph Scott & Larry Davis

Stevie Ray Vaughan's intro to 'Texas Flood' is a masterpiece of modern blues guitar. He wrenches some incredible phrases from his instrument.

His sound is extremely strong — helped by using extra heavy strings and tuning his guitar a semitone flat.

'Texas Flood' is written in G and was played in this position on the guitar but sounds a semitone flat. Listen to the record for a feeling of how to play this piece — it will make sense of the notes on the page.

Intro

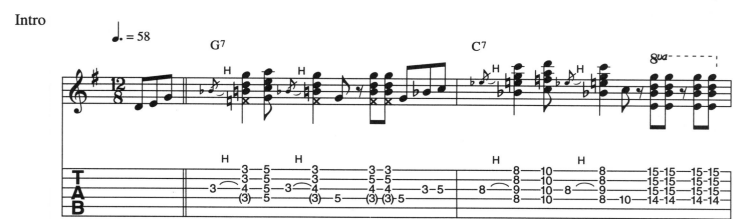

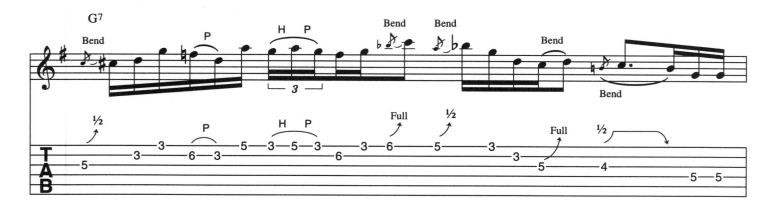

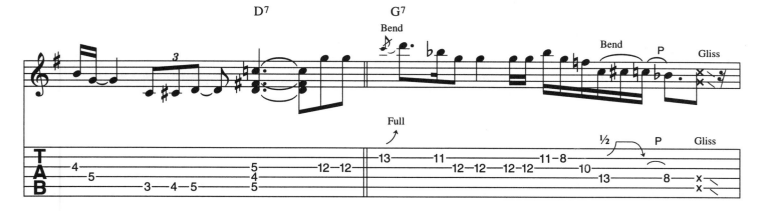

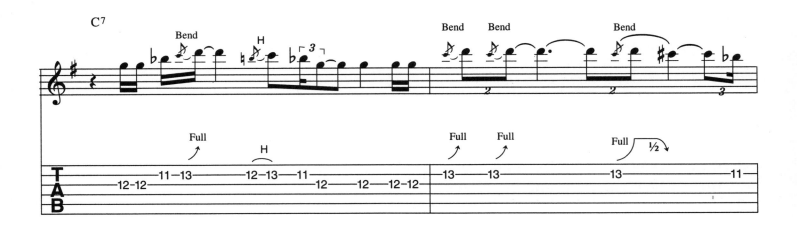

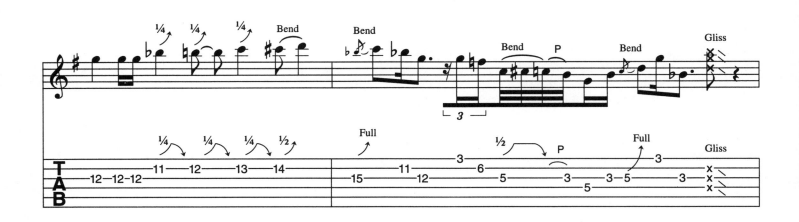

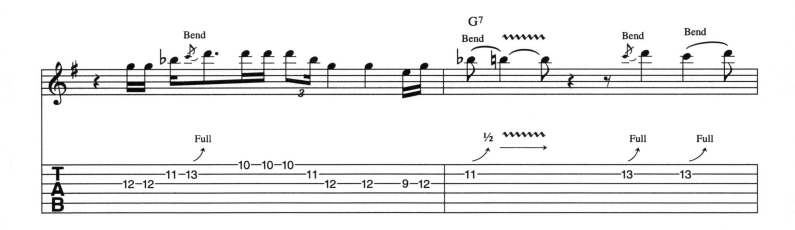

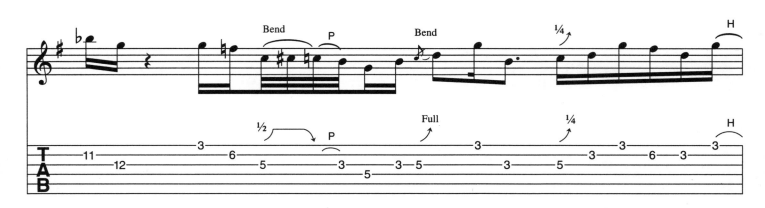

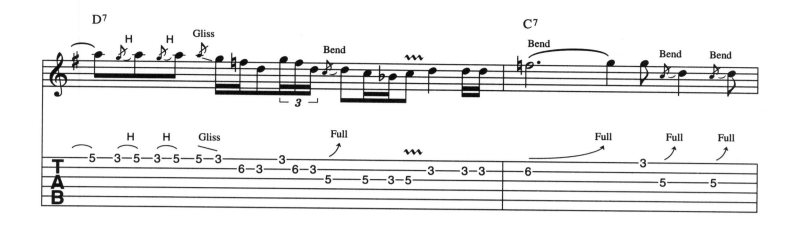

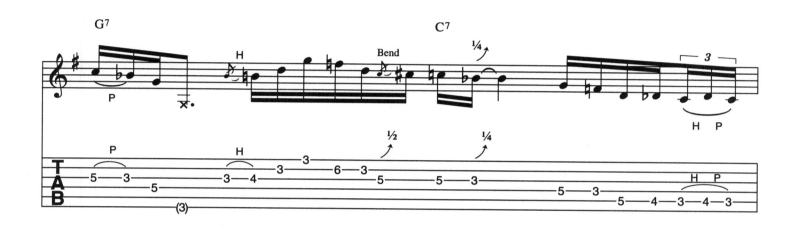

Born Under A Bad Sign
Robben Ford

LP 'Talk To Your Daughter'
Warner Bros. 25647 – 2

Words & Music by Booker T. Jones & William Bell

Robben Ford's sense of timing pays homage to the great blues masters, but by and large he is playing inside the pulse of the music.

The solo contains many classic blues inflections. Ford's bending is never random — notice the first notes here, G bent up to A, the 5th of the tonic chord.

Ford often employs a heavy vibrato on the minor 3rd of the tonic chord, moving between the flattened 3rd, 'the blue note', and the major 3rd.

This ambiguity relates directly to the bass line, which contains F, the minor 3rd of the D chord. This figure is used on all sections of the tune where the tonic chord is used.

Bass Riff Example

Solo

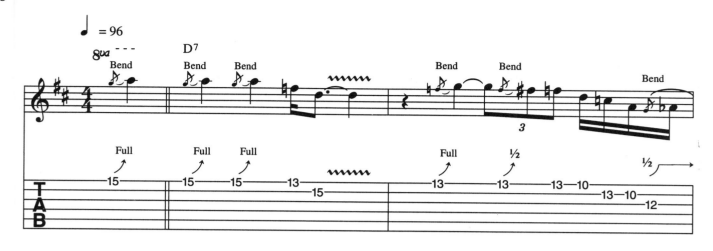

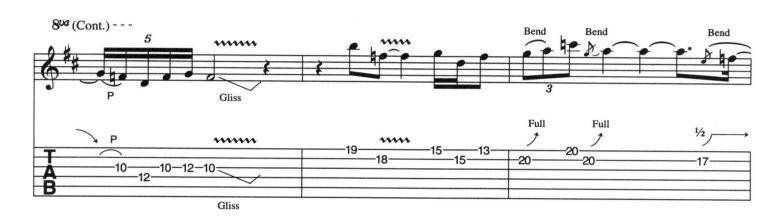

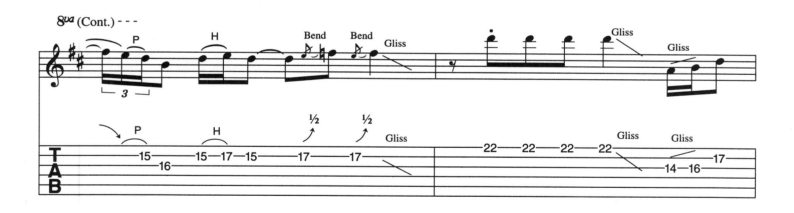

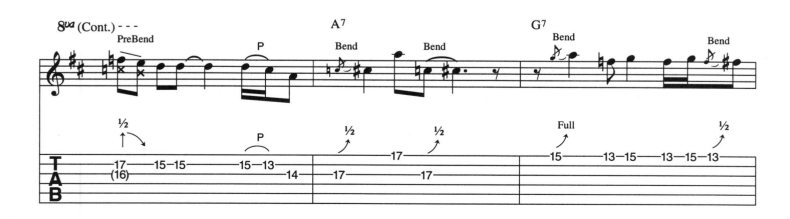

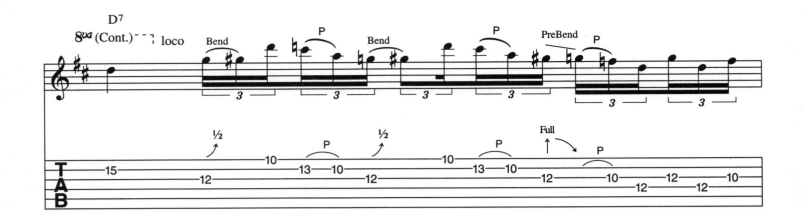

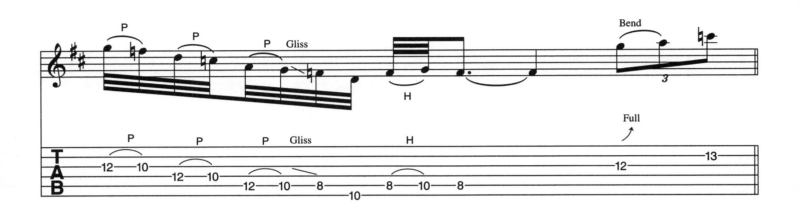

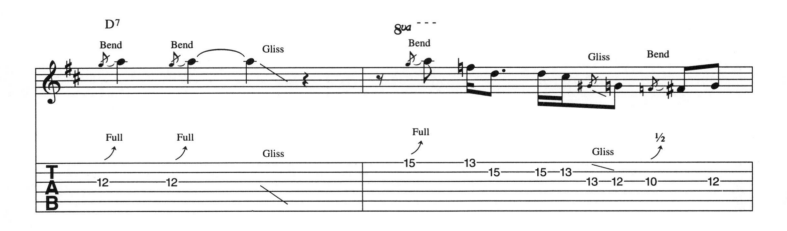

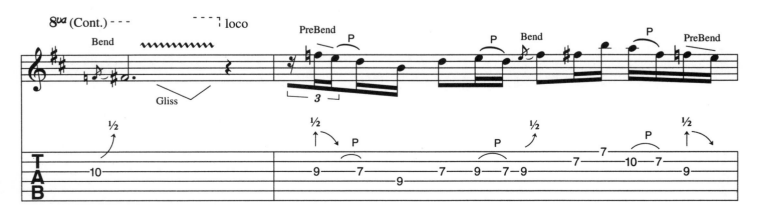

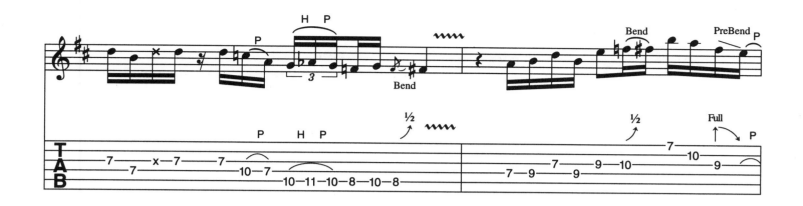

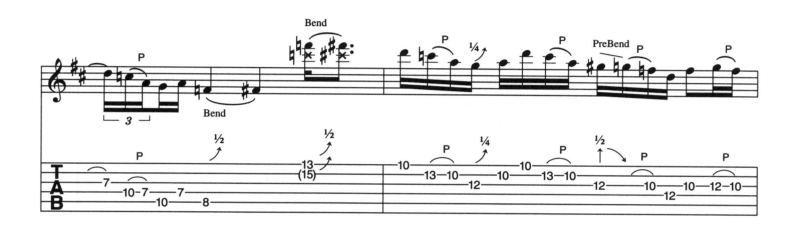

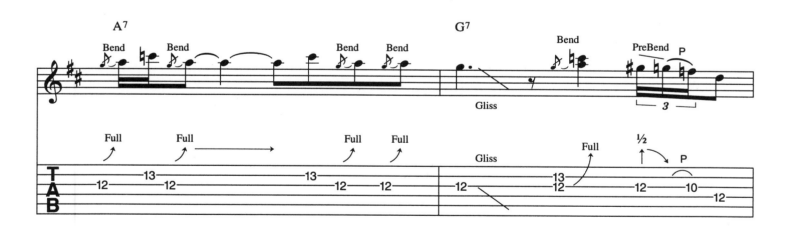

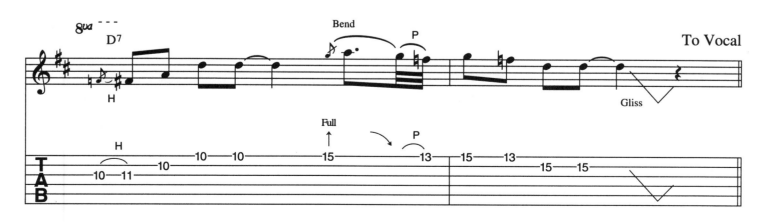

To Vocal

The Stumble

Peter Green

CD 'The Blues Guitar Box Vol.3'
TBB CD 47555/3

Words & Music by Freddie King & Sonny Thompson

Peter Green's 'The Stumble' is a great piece of London blues. Green's edgy sound and aggressive phrasing makes for a really dramatic impression.

Bar 3 is a good E major blues lick. Also note the dead stops in the rhythm section from bar 10. The double stops at bar 13 are interesting as this passage uses both G and G♯, the minor **and** major 3rd. The last 2 bars of the solo are a classic blues turnaround.

Experiment with any part of this solo that you might apply to other songs.

Melody/Solo

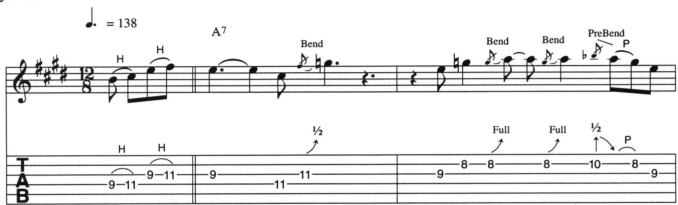

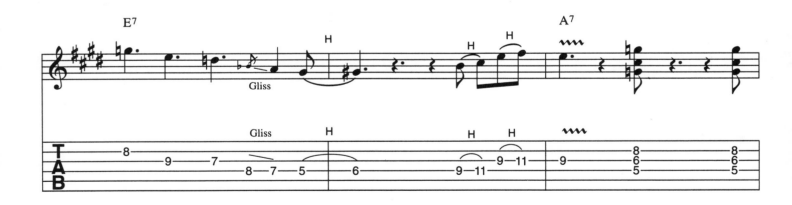

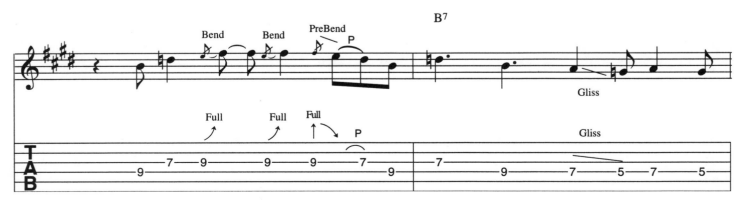

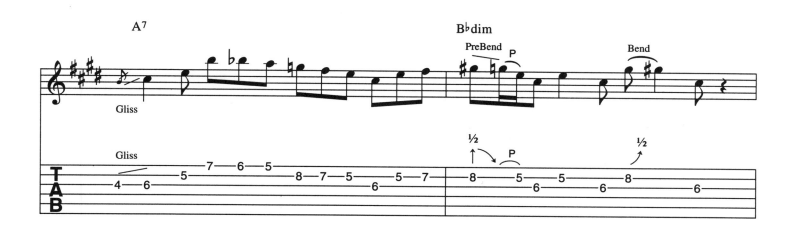

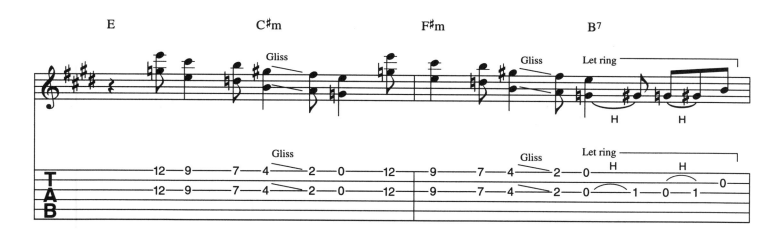

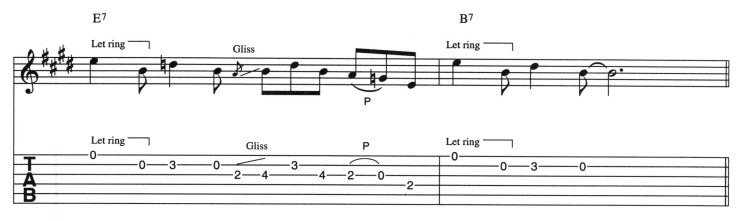

Don't Throw Your Love On Me So Strong

Mike Bloomfield

LP 'The Live Adventures Of Mike Bloomfield and Al Cooper'
Columbia KGP 6

Words & Music by Albert King

Mike Bloomfield's solo on 'Don't Throw Your Love On Me So Strong' looks complicated on paper but if you get a chance to hear the recording, you'll get an idea of his style.

Note that much of the more ornate playing seems to have been executed in one position, for example the blues lick in bar 2.

He manipulates this sixth position idea all through the solo. In fact, Bloomfield is working with quite a small amount of material but makes good use of it. This is a good lesson to learn — you must try to make the best and most imaginative use of whatever musical material you have at your disposal.

Note the Jazz/Gospel chord changes in the intro. The $B\flat^7$, $B\flat^7/D$, $E\flat^7$, E dim progression can be used for the first two bars of a $B\flat$ blues. Each chord = 2 beats.

Let's isolate a small fragment of Bloomfield's solo — it contains the material used for most of his improvisation. Rhythmically, it is distinguished by the use of a short burst of demisemiquavers; harmonically, by the use of the blues scale with added 6th degree.

Fragment

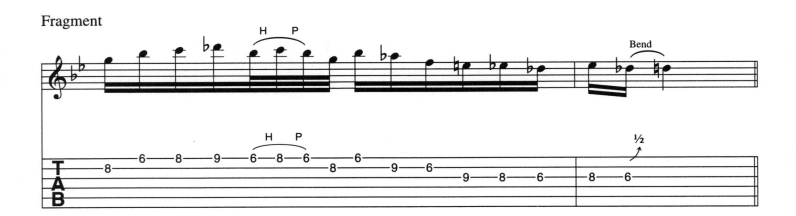

32

Intro

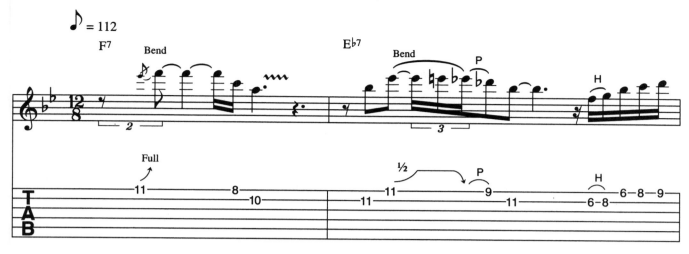

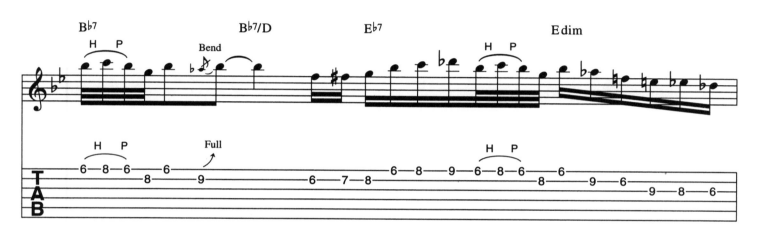

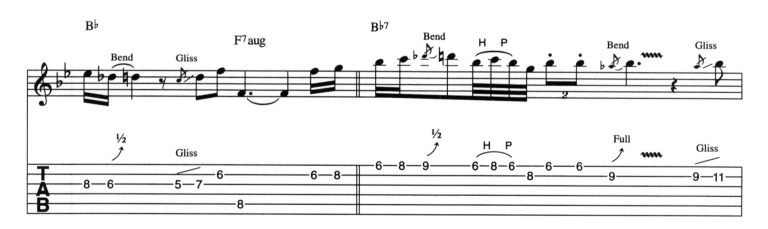

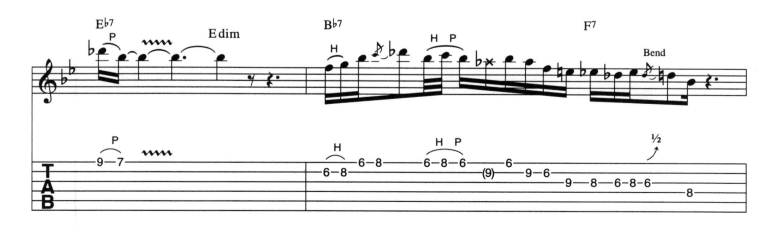

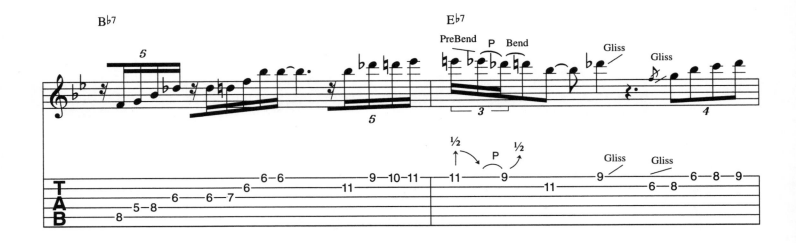

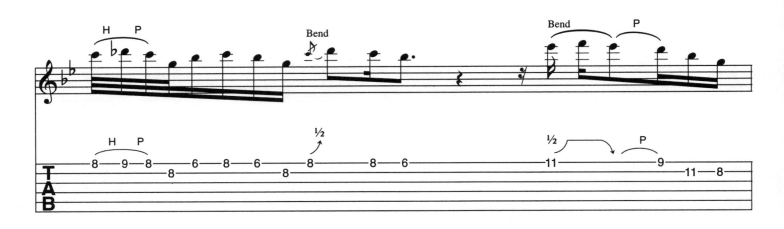

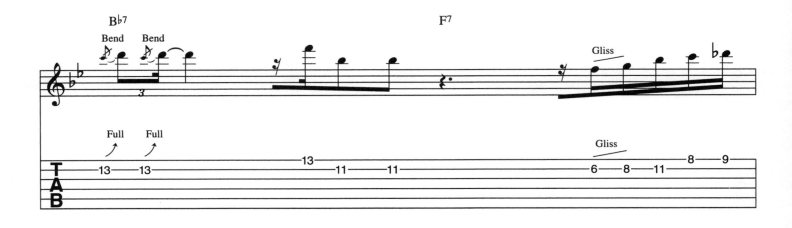

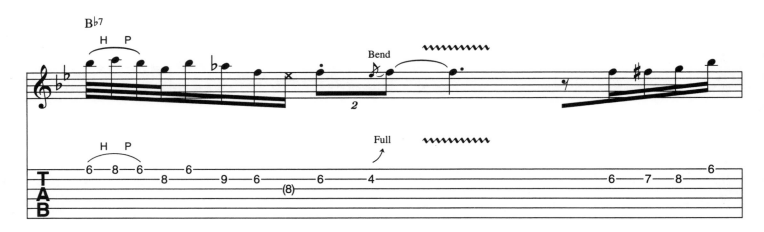

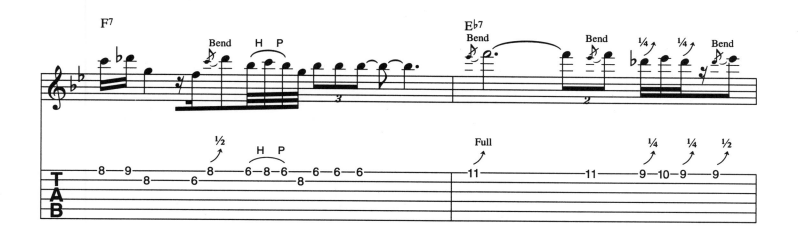

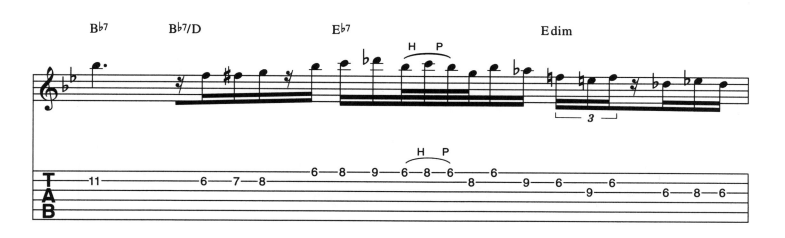

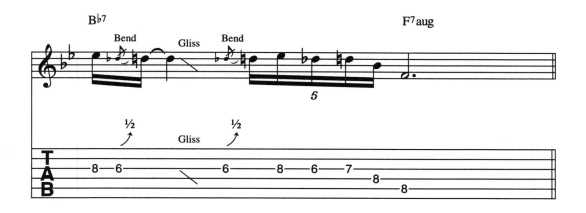

Example 1 exploits the blues scale idea.

Example 1

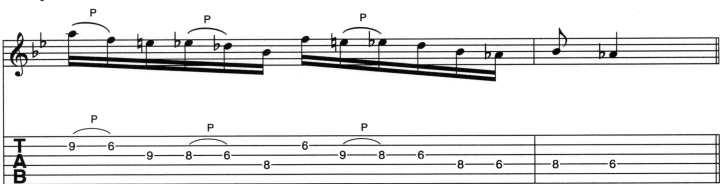

Example 2 uses the characteristic demisemiquaver rhythm.

Example 2

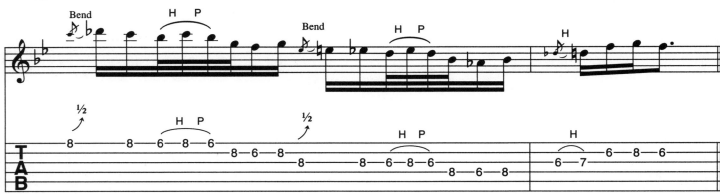

Example 3 is more spacious and emphasises the flattened 3rd and sharpened 4th degrees of the blues scale — both very colourful notes.

Example 3

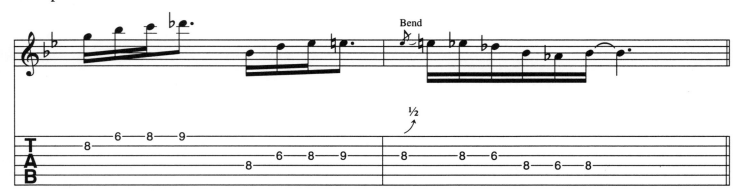

Example 4 introduces some bends for extra blues flavour.

Example 4

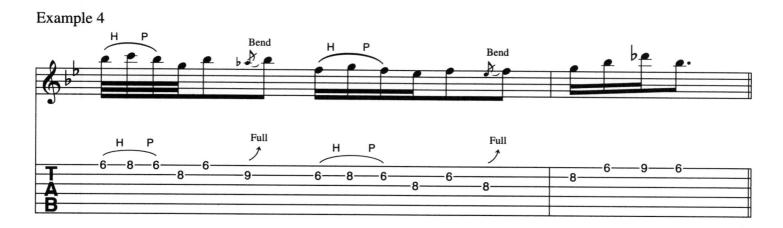

Example 5 is a fairly typical blues lick and milks the flattened 5th interval between the E and B♭.

Example 5

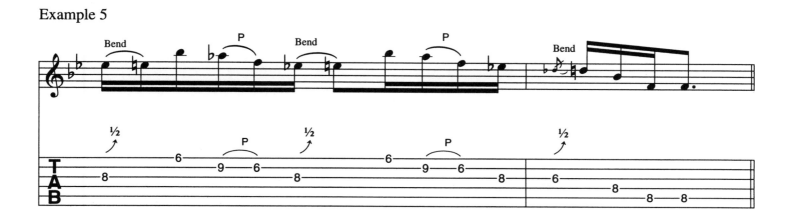

Crosscut Saw
Albert King

CD 'King Of The Blues Guitar'
Atlantic 8213 – 2

Words & Music by R.B. Ford

Albert King's solo on 'Cross Cut Saw' is a beautiful and well-balanced piece of playing. It is lyrical and is another example of a 'conversational' style of delivery.

The first four notes seem to be a call for our attention. The clear use of triplets in bar 10 is a useful device. The last two bars are a typical blues turnaround and can easily be used in other blues settings.

The example shows the bass riff used in 'Cross Cut Saw'. It outlines the major 6th chord and is a common figure. It moves to follow the chords of the song.

Bass Riff Example

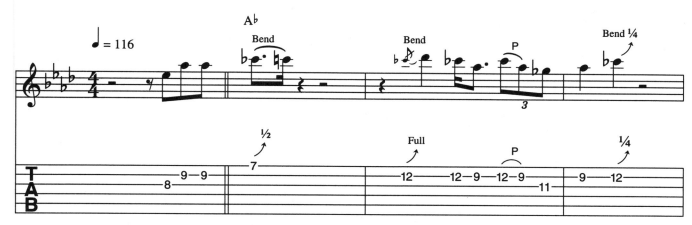

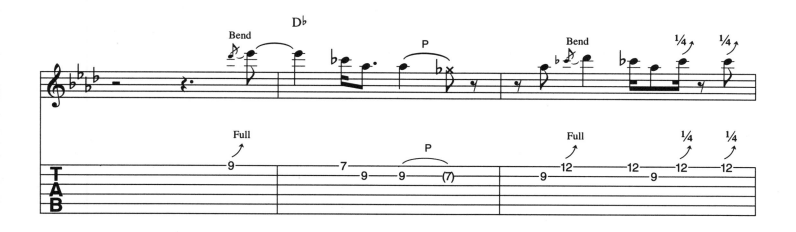

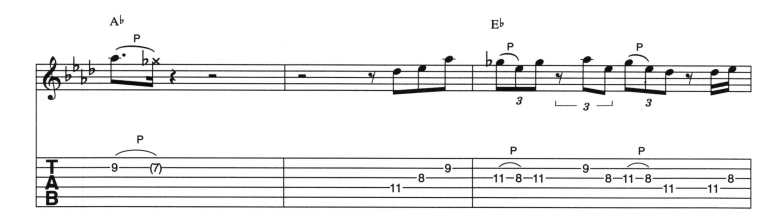

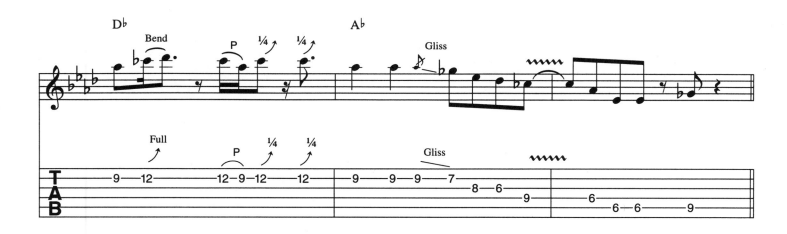

Dust My Broom

Freddie King

LP 'Getting Ready'
A&M AMLS 65004

Words & Music by Robert Johnson

Freddie King plays this Elmore James song on acoustic guitar. The first 4 bars of the Intro are played in typical bottleneck style. At bar 5 the notes are damped with the palm of the pick hand but played open from bar 6 onwards. He plays some classic open string guitar over the A chord in bars 6 to 8 before moving to B⁷ where he moves up to the 5th position in bar 10. Note the open strings in the turnaround bars – allow them to ring over the phrase.

Intro

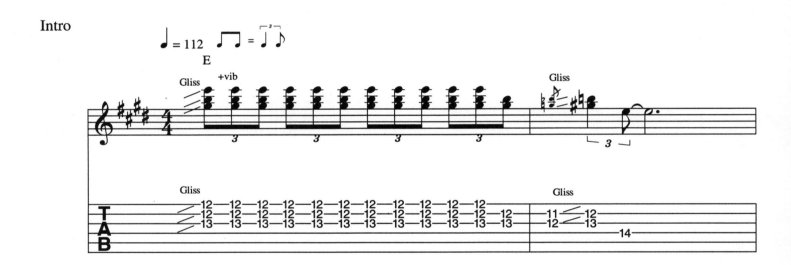

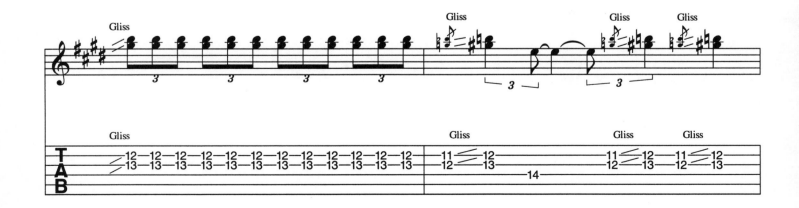

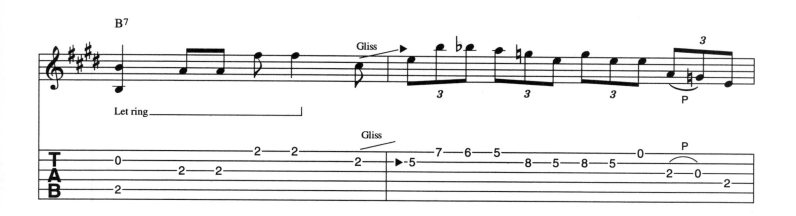

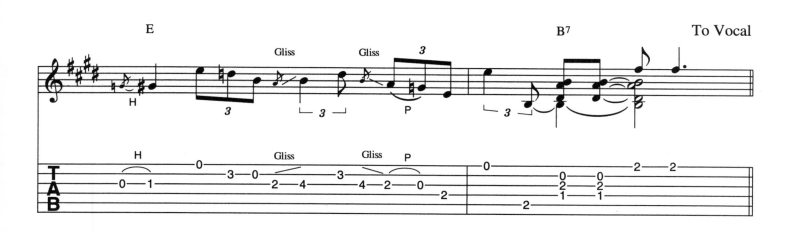

The solo begins with a similar double stopped figure to the one in the Intro. This is followed by an open string answering phrase. The double stopped idea continues with the bending of the G to G♯ on the 2nd string through bars 3 and 4 leading to the A chord and some great Em blues lines which follow.

1st solo

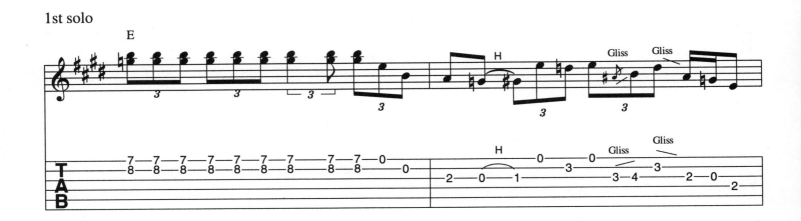

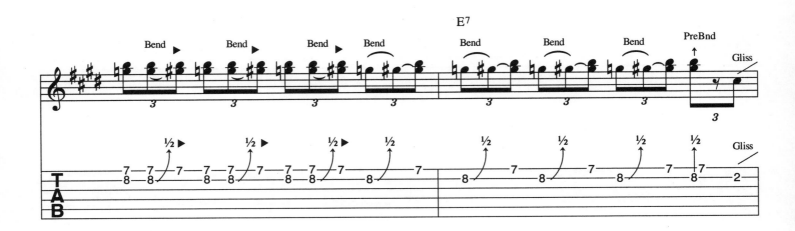

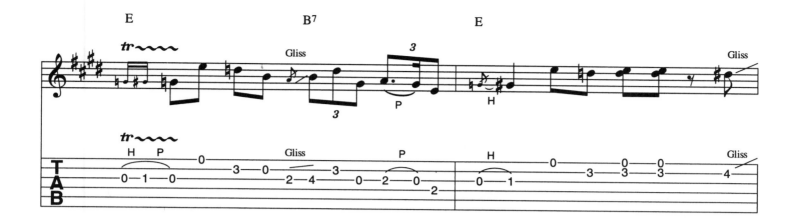

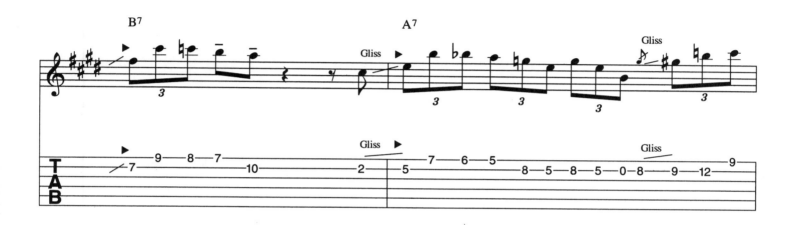

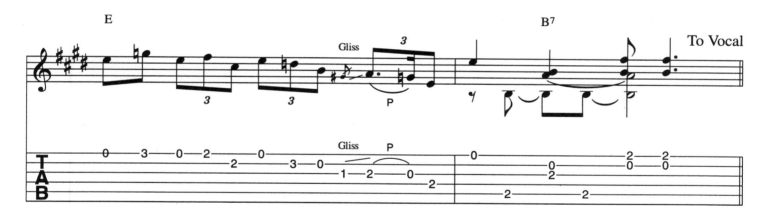

Another of Freddie's great turnaround phrases:

Ending

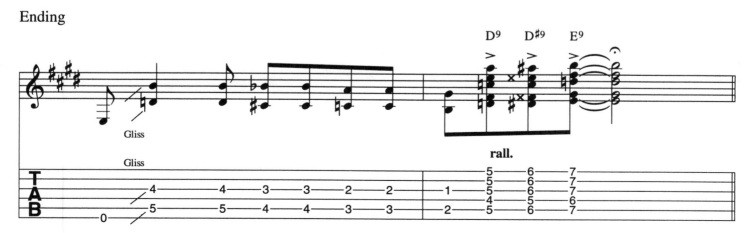

No Money, No Luck Blues

B.B. King

CD 'Lucille'
MCA MCAD – 10518

Words & Music by Ivory Joe Hunter

B.B.King's solo on 'No Money, No Luck Blues' is a lesson in rhythmic variety. He uses all sub-divisions of the beat.

The slow $\frac{12}{8}$ time signature lends itself well to rhythmic ambiguity — particularly between sub-divisions of three and four.

B.B. King always seems to be aware of the chords, note the flattened 7th of E^7 to the major third of B^7.

This awareness of chord tones gives an air of certainty to your music — play through your favourite songs isolating the chord tones.

Let's examine some of the rhythmic possibilities contained in the slow $\frac{12}{8}$ pulse of 'No Money, No Luck Blues'. In example 1a simple quaver subdivisions of the beat are used.

Example 1a

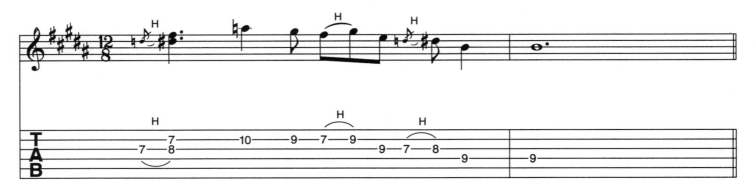

In 1b we use semiquaver subdivisions.

Example 1b

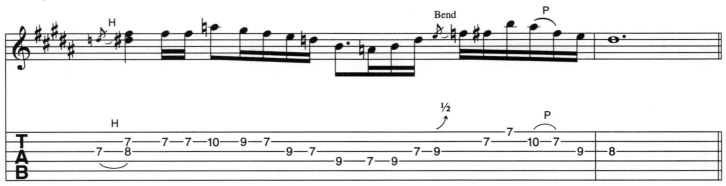

Example 2 includes semiquaver triplets — a common device. This adds 'swing' to the slow $\frac{12}{8}$ feel.

Example 2

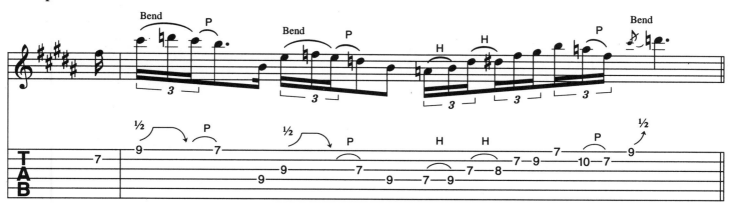

Example 3a demonstrates simple, even divisions of the beat. This is also a common feature of a slow $\frac{12}{8}$ blues solo, suggesting a $\frac{4}{4}$ time signature.

Example 3a

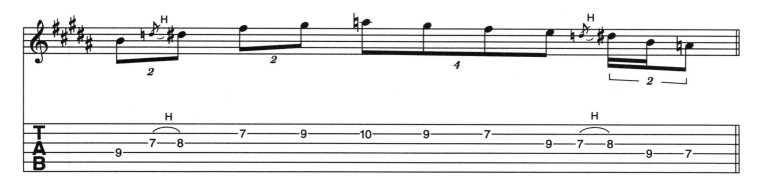

3b integrates even subdivisions with the underlying triplet pulse.

Example 3b

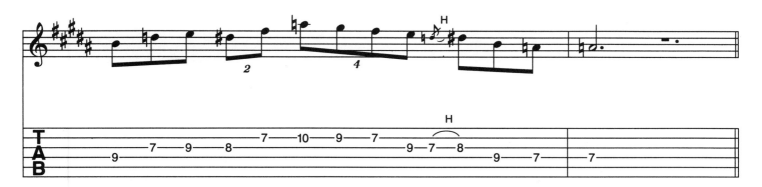

Examples 4a and 4b show a more complex combination of the previous elements.

Example 4a

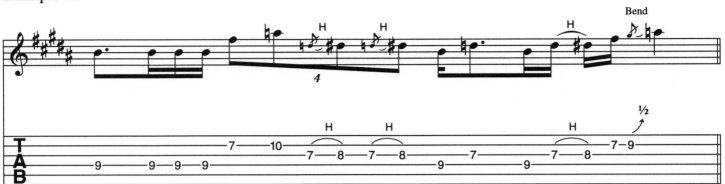

Example 4b

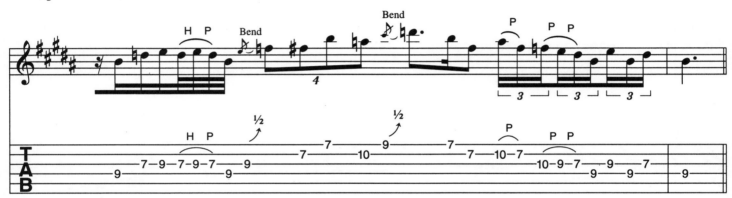

Now try to compose your own licks using all the rhythmic units you have seen here. If the example looks complex, remember this is a slow pulse!

Intro

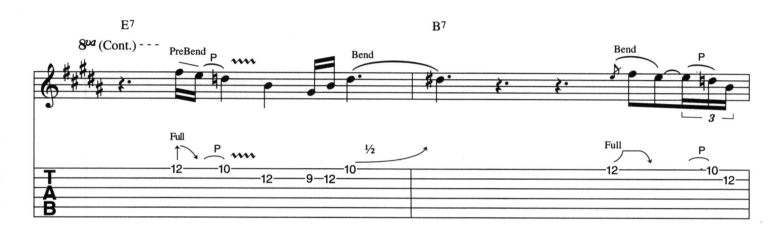

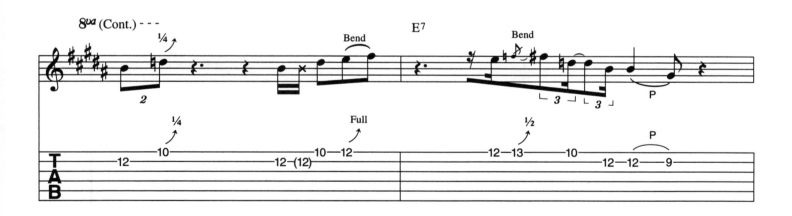

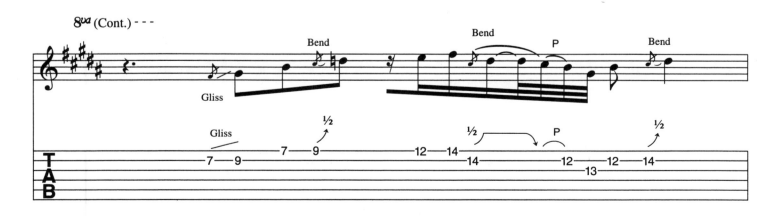

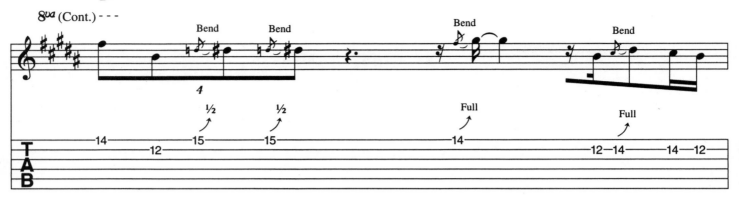